W9-BZS-834

This
Ready Set Read
book belongs to:

My Reading Tree!

For Dave
~ A.H.B.

For Jamie and Joseph
~ G.W.

LITTLE TIGER PRESS
An imprint of Magi Publications
1 The Coda Centre, 189 Munster Road, London SW6 6 AW
www.littletigerpress.com

First published in Great Britain 2000
by Little Tiger Press, London
This edition published 2011
Text copyright © A. H. Benjamin 2000
Illustrations copyright © Gwyneth Williamson 2000

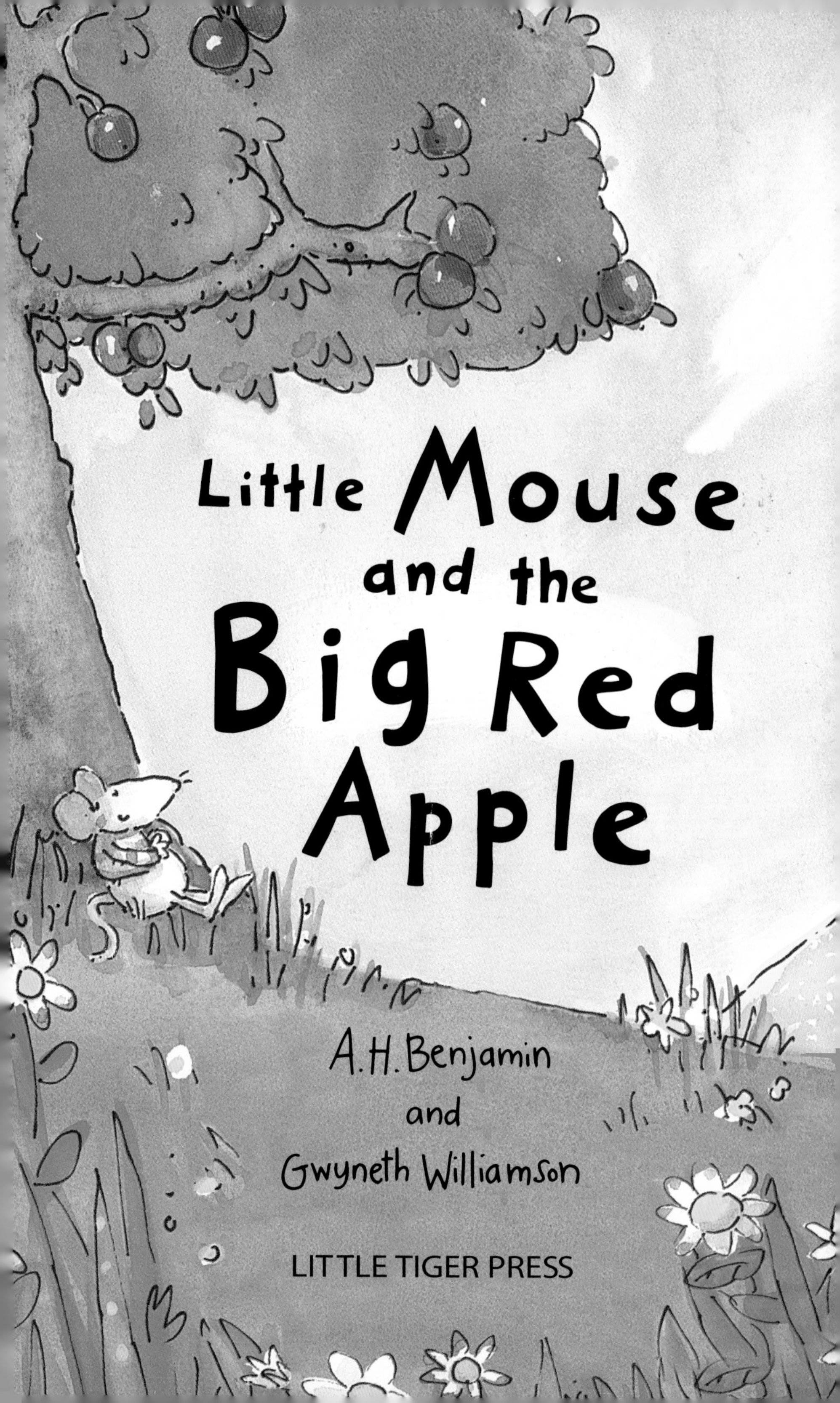

Little Mouse and the Big Red Apple

A. H. Benjamin

and

Gwyneth Williamson

LITTLE TIGER PRESS

Mouse was feeling a bit hungry
one day when all of a sudden he
came across a big, red, juicy apple.
 "That's perfect!" he cried.
"I'll take it home with me and
have a feast!"

Mouse set off toward his little house,
rolling the apple over and over.

He couldn't wait to get his teeth into
the big, red, juicy apple. "Yum, yum,"
he thought, when all of a sudden . . .

. . . the apple rolled into a pond.

"Oh, no!" wailed Mouse. "What am I going to do now?"

"Don't worry," said Frog, hopping out of the water. "I'll help you."

Frog kicked the apple hard with his strong back legs. It flew out of the water and . . .

BUMP!

landed on the ground.

"There you go," said Frog. He licked his lips and stared at the apple.

"Um, thanks," said Mouse, as he began to roll it along the path. He didn't want to share his apple with Frog.

Mouse went on his way, thinking of the lovely apple dinner he would have later. His mouth was already watering when . . .

the big, red, juicy apple fell into a thorn bush.

"Silly me!" muttered Mouse, as he tried to rescue his dinner.

"Ouch, that hurt!" he cried. "Those prickles are sharp!"

"I see you have a problem,"
said Tortoise, trundling up
to Mouse. "Leave it to me."
Tortoise didn't have to worry
about the sharp prickles. He
had his shell to protect him.

Without any trouble at all, Tortoise crept under the thorn bush and brought out the big, red, juicy apple.

"Problem solved!" he said, stroking the apple longingly.

"Easy," said Mole, popping out of a nearby hole. "I'll make you a tunnel."

And she did. She made a tunnel that went right under the hedgehog.

15

It was just wide enough for Mouse
and the apple to go through.

"Always glad to help!" said Mole,
sniffing at the big, red, juicy apple
with her little nose.

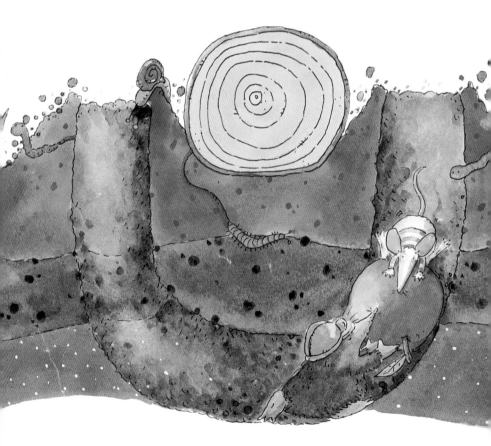

"It's very kind of you," said Mouse,
and he went on his way as fast as
he could. He did not want to share
the apple with Mole.

He rolled the apple over and
over until . . .

PuSH

PuSH

. . . he came to
a steep hill.
His house was
at the very top.

Push, push,
heave, heave,
went Mouse,
grunting and
groaning.

HEAVE
HEAVE

Up, up, up
he went, until
he reached the
very top.

"At last!" sighed
Mouse happily.
"Time for that lovely
apple meal!" But as
Mouse let go . . .

19

. . . the apple wobbled,
and then it started to
roll down the other
side of the hill!

It rolled
faster and
faster . . .

farther
and farther,
until . . .

. . . it came to a stop
at the bottom of the hill.
Mouse could see it lying there,
like a big, red jewel.

"Oh, no," he cried, "I will
have to start all over again!"

Mouse scurried down the
hill on his little, tired feet.

Faster and faster he ran.
But when he reached the bottom . . .

. . . he found Frog, Mole, and Tortoise
had gotten there first!

"How kind of you to send
that apple all the way back to us,"
called out Mole, chomping away on a
piece of it.

Mouse let out a big sigh.
"Don't mention it," he said.
"Isn't that what friends are for?"

Picture Dictionary

Look at the words below and put the correct
picture sticker next to each word.

frog   apple

tree   bird

Have you got these right?
Then put a star on your reading tree!

Amazing Alphabet

a b c d e f g h i j k l m n
o p q r s t u v w x y z

Put the word stickers in alphabetical order,
using the alphabet above to help.

log – dinner – tunnel – pond – bush – hill

1) _____   2) _____   3) _____

4) _____   5) _____   6) _____

Did you get this right?
Add another star to your reading tree!

Cool Vowels and Consonants

The alphabet is made up of vowels and consonants.

Vowels sound soft. They are: a e i o u (and sometimes y).

Consonants sound harder. They are:
b c d f g h j k l m n p q r s t v w x y z.

1) Circle the words that begin with a vowel.

over	feast	apple
shell	up	red

2) Circle the words that begin with a consonant.

share	off	out
thorn	until	bush

3) Circle the words that begin with a consonant and end with a vowel.

mouse	sudden	voice
home	thought	legs

4) Circle the words that begin with a vowel and end with a consonant.

under	fast	again
happily	ouch	wide

Did you spot the vowels and consonants?
Add a star to your reading tree!

27

Awesome Adjectives

An **adjective** is a describing word. Add the missing adjectives to the sentences from the story below using the word stickers.

> tired – red – little – juicy – big

1) Mouse set off toward his _____ house, rolling the apple over and over.

2) He couldn't wait to get his teeth into the big, red, _____ apple.

3) Mouse could see it lying there, like a big, _____ jewel.

4) Mouse scurried down the hill on his little, _____ feet.

5) Mouse let out a _____ sigh.

Did you get all the adjectives right? Great! Add another star to your reading tree.

28

Cool Questions

Some sentences are questions.
You know when a sentence is a question because
it has a **question mark** (?) at the end of it.

Put a **question mark** at the end of the sentences that
are questions. Put a **period** at the end of the
sentences that are not questions.

1) What am I going to do now

2) I'll help you

3) How do I get around that

4) His house was at the very top

5) Isn't that what friends are for

Did you get these right?
Remember to add another
star to your reading tree!

29

Same Meanings

Match the words on the left to the words on the right that have the same meaning. We've done the first one for you.

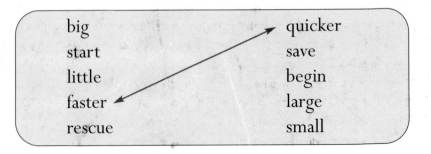

big   quicker
start   save
little   begin
faster   large
rescue   small

Did you match the words?
Add another star to your reading tree.

Busy Verbs

A **verb** is an action word. Add the missing verbs from the **Busy Verbs** stickers to these sentences from the story.

share – licked – scurried – rolled

1) He _____ his lips and stared at the apple.

2) He did not want to _____ his apple with Tortoise.

3) He _____ the apple over and over until . . .

4) Mouse _____ down the hill on his little, tired feet

Did you get all the verbs right? Great!
Add the last star to your reading tree!